STAR WARS

CLONE WARS
VOLUME 2

The events in this story take place between three months to five months after the battle of Geonosis (as seen in *Star Wars: Attack of the Clones*) ◆

STAR WARS®

CLONE WARS
VOLUME 2

Victories and Sacrifices

Dark Horse Books™

colors by **Joe Wayne**

lettering by **Digital Chameleon**

cover illustration by **Carlo Arellano**

publisher **Mike Richardson**

collection designers **Darin Fabrick & Amy Arendts**

art director **Mark Cox**

assistant editor **Jeremy Barlow**

editor **Randy Stradley**

special thanks to **Sue Rostoni** and
Lucy Autrey Wilson at Lucas Licensing

STAR WARS®:CLONE WARS VOLUME 2

THIS VOLUME COLLECTS #51-53 OF *STAR WARS: REPUBLIC* AND *JEDI: SHAAK TI.*

PUBLISHED BY DARK HORSE BOOKS, A DIVISION OF DARK HORSE COMICS, INC.
10956 SE MAIN STREET · MILWAUKIE, OR 97222

WWW.DARKHORSE.COM   WWW.STARWARS.COM
To find a comics shop in your area, call the Comic Shop Locator Service
toll-free at 1-888-266-4226

FIRST EDITION: ISBN: 1-56971-969-1

3 5 7 9 10 8 6 4 2

PRINTED IN CHINA

illustration by **BRIAN CHING**

THE NEW FACE OF WAR

APPROXIMATELY TEN WEEKS
AFTER THE BATTLE OF GEONOSIS...

"The New Face of War"
written by **Haden Blackman**
pencilled by **Tomás Giorello**
inks by **Curtis Arnold**

"Dear Padmé...

"...I still can't get used to being so close, yet so far away from you.

"We're in orbit around Naboo and I should be preparing for our mission, but I've spent all my time wishing that I could put your world in my hand ... to protect it...

"...and you.

"But I can't — not while I'm fighting in the Clone Wars!"

ANAKIN, YOU'RE BROODING AGAIN? I'VE ALREADY TOLD YOU THAT PADMÉ WILL BE FINE. THE DISTURBANCE IS STILL CONFINED TO THE MOON.

"Padmè, my love,

"...edi aren't supposed ...feel fear, but I am ...raid.

"I'm afraid for you.

"The Confederacy has turned Ohma-d'un into a graveyard...

"...and Naboo is next.

"I just want to abandon my mission and fly to you...

"...but there are innocents here who still need to be rescued.

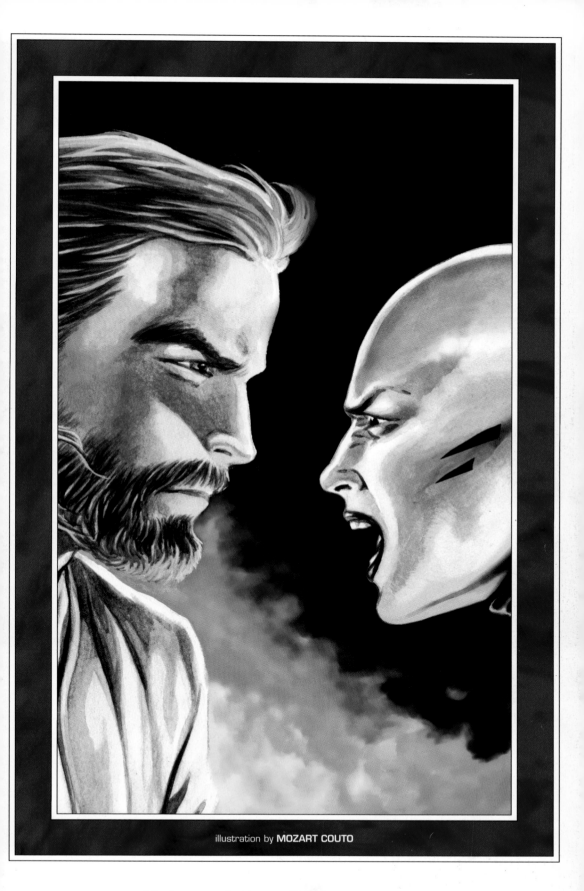

illustration by **MOZART COUTO**

BLAST RADIUS

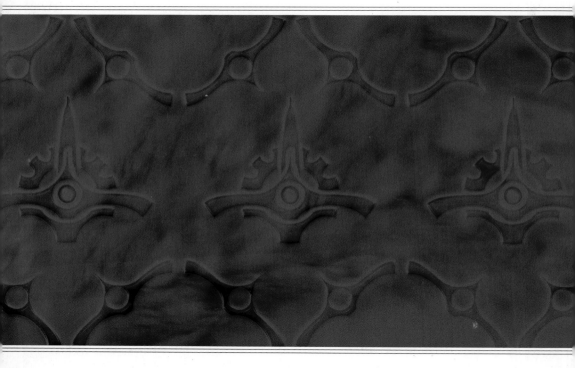

"Blast Radius"
written by **Haden Blackman**
pencilled by **Brian Ching**
inks by **Joe Weems**

HE'S RECOVERING?

YES. THANK THE FORCE YOUR MASTER SURVIVED HIS MISSION.

WHAT *WAS* HIS MISSION, MASTER WINDU?

THIS. IT'S AN *ANTIDOTE* TO THE CONFEDERACY'S CHEMICAL WEAPON THAT YOU ENCOUNTERED ON OHMA-D'UN.

THAT GAS *COULD* HAVE BEEN THE KEY TO THE CONFEDERACY'S VICTORY --

-- THEY COULD HAVE WIPED OUT THE REPUBLIC'S ARMIES WITHOUT HARMING THEIR OWN DROID TROOPS. BUT WITH THIS ANTIDOTE, THE WEAPON IS USELESS.

AND ONLY FOUR JEDI DIED TO BRING IT TO US...

...THEY WILL BE DEEPLY MISSED.

"BUT *NO ONE* HATED *MASTER FAY*. QUI-GON SPOKE OF HER ONCE... HE CALLED HER BEAUTIFUL AND AGELESS..."

THEY WERE THE *NOMADS* OF THE JEDI ORDER, RARELY COMING TO CORUSCANT, BUT FIGHTING FOR PEACE AND FREEDOM ACROSS THE STARS.

I HADN'T MET ANY OF THEM BEFORE THIS MISSION. I HAD ONLY HEARD THE STORIES...

NOT *STORIES*, MASTER KENOBI. *HISTORIES*.

NOW, TELL US HOW THEIR HISTORIES *ENDED*.

"IN ALL HER LONG DECADES, SHE NEVER RAISED HER LIGHTSABER IN COMBAT. I DON'T EVEN KNOW IF SHE *CARRIED* ONE..."

"AS YOU KNOW, AFTER ANAKIN AND I HAD THE ENCOUNTER WITH THE ASSASSIN *DURGE* AND *COMMANDER ASAJJ VENTRESS* ON THE MOON OF *OHMA-D'UN*, ORDERS WENT OUT TO FIND THE *SOURCE* OF THE CONFEDERACY'S CHEMICAL WEAPON..."

"MY SEARCH TOOK ME TO THE PLANET *QUEYTA*, WHERE THE OTHER JEDI WERE ALREADY WAITING. SOME HAD FOLLOWED THEIR *OWN* EVIDENCE TRAILS TO THAT DESOLATE WORLD, OTHERS HAD FOLLOWED THE LIVING FORCE..."

illustration by **JAN DUURSEMA**

CATSPAW

"Catspaw"
written by **John Ostrander**
pencilled by **Jan Duursema**
inked by **Dan Parsons**

SAD SOUL. WHAT WERE YOU THINKING? WERE YOU *DEFENDING* US? OR WERE YOU SIMPLY LASHING OUT, TAKING LIFE AS LIFE WAS TAKEN FROM YOU?

IF I AM ABLE, I WILL COME BACK, RYYK. YOUR BODY WILL BE RECLAIMED AND SENT TO KASHYYYK. YOU WILL BE MOURNED AND REMEMBERED. NO MORE THAN THIS CAN I DO FOR YOU.

WE NEED TO PUSH ON, GENERAL.

I KNOW.

WE ALSO HAVE COME AS FAR AS WE CAN TOGETHER. IT'S TIME TO SPLIT OUR FORCES.

TROOPER, SINCE WE HAVE LOST THE WOOKIEE, YOU WILL HAVE TO ATTACK THE SHIELD GENERATOR ON YOUR OWN.

VOS, YOU AND AUTEM MUST DISABLE THE TOWER CANNONS BEFORE THE SECOND ATTACK IS LAUNCHED.

THE TROOPER CAN TRAVEL WITH US A BIT FURTHER BEFORE HE HAS TO SPLIT OFF.

"GOOD. LYSHAA AND I WILL CAPTURE SHOGAR TOK.

"REMEMBER, ONLY ONE MISSION *NEEDS* TO SUCCEED -- BUT AT LEAST ONE *MUST* SUCCEED. THERE IS NOT MUCH TIME."

CLONE WARS
TIMELINE

MONTHS
(AFTER ATTACK OF THE CLONES)

0	**THE BATTLE OF GEONOSIS**	
	Star Wars: Episode II — *Attack of the Clones* (LF, May '02)	
0	**THE SEARCH FOR COUNT DOOKU**	
	Boba Fett #1: *The Fight to Survive* (SB, April '02)	
+1	**THE BATTLE OF RAXUS PRIME**	
	Boba Fett #2: *Crossfire* (SB, November '02)	
+1	**THE DARK REAPER PROJECT**	
	The Clone Wars (LA, May '03)	
+1.5	**CONSPIRACY ON AARGAU**	
	Boba Fett #3: *Maze of Deception* (SB, April '03)	
+2	**THE BATTLE OF KAMINO**	
	Clone Wars I: *The Defense of Kamino* (DH, June '03)	
+2	**DURGE VS BOBA FETT**	
	Boba Fett #4: *Hunted* (SB, October '03)	
+3	**THE DEFENSE OF NABOO**	
	Clone Wars II: *Victories and Sacrifices* (DH, September '03)	
+6	**THE DEVARON RUSE**	
	Clone Wars IV: *Light and Dark* (DH, May '04)	
+6	**THE HARUUN KAL CRISIS**	
	Shatterpoint (DR, June '03)	
+12	**THE BIO-DROID THREAT**	
	The Cestus Deception (DR, June '04)	
+15	**THE BATTLE OF JABIIM**	
	Clone Wars III: *Last Stand on Jabiim* (DH, February '04)	
+24	**THE CASUALTIES OF DRONGAR**	
	MEDSTAR DUOLOGY	
	Battle Surgeons (DR, July '04) *Jedi Healer* (DR, October '04)	
+30	**THE PRAESITLYN CONQUEST**	
	Jedi Trial (DR, November '04)	

ABBREVIATION KEY

DH = Dark Horse Comics, graphic novels www.darkhorse.com
DR = Del Rey, hardcover and paperback novels www.delreydigital.com
LA = LucasArts Games, games for XBox, Game Cube, PS2, and PC platforms
www.lucasarts.com
LF = Lucasfilm Ltd., motion pictures www.starwars.com
SB = Scholastic Books, juvenile fiction www.scholastic.com/starwars

TALES OF THE SITH ERA
25,000-1000 YEARS
BEFORE STAR WARS:
A NEW HOPE

TALES OF THE JEDI
THE GOLDEN AGE OF THE SITH
Anderson • Carrasco, Jr. • Gossett
ISBN: 1-56971-229-8 $16.95
FALL OF THE SITH EMPIRE
Anderson • Heike • Carrasco, Jr.
ISBN: 1-56971-320-0 $14 .95
KNIGHTS OF THE OLD REPUBLIC
Veitch • Gossett
ISBN: 1-56971-020-1 $14.95
THE FREEDON NADD UPRISING
Veitch • Akins • Rodier
ISBN: 1-56971-307-3 $5.95
DARK LORDS OF THE SITH
Veitch • Anderson • Gossett
ISBN: 1-56971-095-3 $17.95
THE SITH WAR
Anderson • Carrasco, Jr.
ISBN: 1-56971-173-9 $17.95

*REDEMPTION
Anderson • Gossett • Pepoy • McDaniel
ISBN: 1-56971-535-1 $14.95

*JEDI VS. SITH
Macan • Bachs • Fernandez
ISBN: 1-56971-649-8 $15.95

PREQUEL ERA 1000-0
YEARS BEFORE STAR
WARS: A NEW HOPE

*JEDI COUNCIL
ACTS OF WAR
Stradley • Fabbri • Vecchia
ISBN: 1-56971-539-4 $12.95

*DARTH MAUL
Marz • Duursema • Magyar • Struzan
ISBN: 1-56971-542-4 $12.95

PRELUDE
TO REBELLION
Strnad • Winn • Jones
ISBN: 1-56971-448-7 $14.95
OUTLANDER
Truman • Leonardi • Rio
ISBN: 1-56971-514-9 $14.95
*JEDI COUNCIL
EMMISSARIES
TO MALASTARE
Truman • Duursema • Others
ISBN: 1-56971-545-9 $15.95

STAR WARS:
TWILIGHT
Ostrander • Duursema • Magyar
ISBN: 1-56971-558-0 $12.95
EPISODE 1 —
THE PHANTOM MENACE
Gilroy • Damaggio • Williamson
ISBN: 1-56971-359-6 $12.95
EPISODE 1 —
THE PHANTOM
MENACE ADVENTURES
ISBN: 1-56971-443-6 $12.95

MANGA EDITIONS
Translated into English
EPISODE 1 —
THE PHANTOM MENACE
George Lucas • Kia Asamiya
VOLUME 1
ISBN: 1-56971-483-5 $9.95
VOLUME 2
ISBN: 1-56971-484-3 $9.95

*JANGO FETT
Marz • Fowler
ISBN: 1-56971-623-4 $5.95

*ZAM WESELL
Marz • Naifeh
ISBN: 1-56971-624-2 $5.95

EPISODE 2 —
ATTACK OF THE CLONES
Gilroy • Duursema • Kryssing • McCaig
ISBN: 1-56971-609-9 $17.95
DROIDS
THE KALARBA ADVENTURES
Thorsland • Windham • Gibson
ISBN: 1-56971-064-3 $17.95
REBELLION
Windham • Gibson
ISBN: 1-56971-224-7 $14.95

JABBA THE HUTT
THE ART OF THE DEAL
Woodring • Wetherell • Sheldon
ISBN: 1-56971-310-3 $9.95
*UNDERWORLD
THE YAVIN VASSILIKA
Kennedy • Meglia
ISBN: 1-56971-618-8 $14.95
CLASSIC STAR WARS
HAN SOLO AT STARS' END
Goodwin • Alcala
ISBN: 1-56971-254-9 $6.95
BOBA FETT
ENEMY OF THE EMPIRE
Wagner • Gibson • Nadeau • Ezquerra
ISBN: 1-56971-407-X $12.95

TRILOGY ERA
0-5 YEARS
AFTER STAR WARS:
A NEW HOPE

A NEW HOPE SPECIAL EDITION
Jones • Barreto • Williamson
ISBN: 1-56971-213-1 $9.95
MANGA EDITIONS
Translated into English
A NEW HOPE
George Lucas • Hisao Tamaki
VOLUME 1
ISBN: 1-56971-362-6 $9.95
VOLUME 2
ISBN: 1-56971-363-4 $9.95
VOLUME 3
ISBN: 1-56971-364-2 $9.95
VOLUME 4
ISBN: 1-56971-365-0 $9.95
VADER'S QUEST
Macan • Gibbons
ISBN: 1-56971-415-0 $11.95

CLASSIC STAR WARS
THE EARLY ADVENTURES
Manning • Hoberg
ISBN: 1-56971-178-X $19.95
SPLINTER OF
THE MIND'S EYE
Austin • Sprouse
ISBN: 1-56971-223-9 $14.95
CLASSIC STAR WARS
IN DEADLY PURSUIT
Goodwin • Williamson
ISBN: 1-56971-109-7 $16.95
THE EMPIRE STRIKES BACK
SPECIAL EDITION
Goodwin • Williamson
ISBN: 1-56971-234-4 $9.95
MANGA EDITIONS
Translated into English
THE EMPIRE STRIKES BACK
George Lucas • Toshiki Kudo
VOLUME 1
ISBN: 1-56971-390-1 $9.95

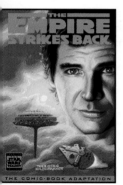

VOLUME 2
ISBN: 1-56971-391-X $9.95
VOLUME 3
ISBN: 1-56971-392-8 $9.95
VOLUME 4
ISBN: 1-56971-393-6 $9.95
CLASSIC STAR WARS
THE REBEL STORM
Goodwin • Williamson
ISBN: 1-56971-106-2 $16.95
CLASSIC STAR WARS
ESCAPE TO HOTH
Goodwin • Williamson
ISBN: 1-56971-093-7 $16.95
SHADOWS OF THE EMPIRE
SHADOWS OF THE EMPIRE
Wagner • Plunkett • Russell
ISBN: 1-56971-183-6 $17.95
RETURN OF THE JEDI
SPECIAL EDITION
Goodwin • Williamson
ISBN: 1-56971-235-2 $9.95
MANGA EDITIONS
Translated into English
RETURN OF THE JEDI
George Lucas • Shin-ichi Hiromoto

VOLUME 1
ISBN: 1-56971-394-4 $9.95
VOLUME 2
ISBN: 1-56971-395-2 $9.95
VOLUME 3
ISBN: 1-56971-396-0 $9.95
VOLUME 4
ISBN: 1-56971-397-9 $9.95

CLASSIC SPIN-OFF ERA
5-25 YEARS
AFTER STAR WARS:
A NEW HOPE

MARA JADE
BY THE EMPEROR'S HAND
Zahn • Stackpole • Ezquerra
ISBN: 1-56971-401-0 $15.95

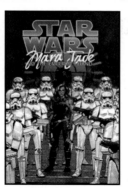

SHADOWS OF THE EMPIRE
EVOLUTION
Perry • Randall • Simmons
ISBN: 1-56971-441-X $14.95
X-WING ROGUE SQUADRON
THE PHANTOM AFFAIR
Stackpole • Macan • Biukovic
ISBN: 1-56971-251-4 $12.95

BATTLEGROUND: TATOOINE
Stackpole • Strnad • Nadeau • Ensign
ISBN: 1-56971-276-X $12.95
THE WARRIOR PRINCESS
Stackpole • Tolson • Nadeau • Ensign
ISBN: 1-56971-330-8 $12.95

REQUIEM FOR A ROGUE
Stackpole • Strnad • Barr • Erskine
ISBN: 1-56971-331-6 $12.95
IN THE EMPIRE'S SERVICE
Stackpole • Nadeau • Ensign
ISBN: 1-56971-383-9 $12.95
BLOOD AND HONOR
Stackpole • Crespo • Hall • Martin
ISBN: 1-56971-387-1 $12.95
MASQUERADE
Stackpole • Johnson • Martin
ISBN: 1-56971-487-8 $12.95

MANDATORY RETIREMENT
Stackpole • Crespo • Nadeau
ISBN: 1-56971-492-4 $12.95
THE THRAWN TRILOGY
HEIR TO THE EMPIRE
Baron • Vatine • Blanchard
ISBN: 1-56971-202-6 $19.95
DARK FORCE RISING
Baron • Dodson • Nowlan
ISBN: 1-56971-269-7 $17.95
THE LAST COMMAND
Baron • Biukovic • Shanower
ISBN: 1-56971-378-2 $17.95
DARK EMPIRE
DARK EMPIRE
Veitch • Kennedy
ISBN: 1-56971-073-2 $17.95
DARK EMPIRE II
Veitch • Kennedy
ISBN: 1-56971-119-4 $17.95
EMPIRE'S END
Veitch • Baikie
ISBN: 1-56971-306-5 $5.95

BOBA FETT
DEATH, LIES,
& TREACHERY
Wagner • Kennedy
ISBN: 1-56971-311-1 $12.95
CRIMSON EMPIRE
CRIMSON EMPIRE
Richardson • Stradley • Gulacy •
Russell
ISBN: 1-56971-355-3 $17.95

COUNCIL OF BLOOD
Richardson • Stradley • Gulacy •
Emberlin
ISBN: 1-56971-410-X $17.95
JEDI ACADEMY
LEVIATHAN
Anderson • Carrasco • Heike
ISBN: 1-56971-456-8 $11.95

THE NEW JEDI ORDER ERA
25+ YEARS
AFTER STAR WARS:
A NEW HOPE

UNION
Stackpole • Teranishi • Chuckry
ISBN: 1-56971-464-9 $12.95

CHEWBACCA
Macan • Duursema • Others
ISBN: 1-56971-515-7 $12.95

INFINITIES — DOES
NOT APPLY TO TIMELINE

*TALES VOLUME 1
Marz • Plunkett • Duursema • Others
ISBN: 1-56971-619-6 $19.95
*INFINITIES — A NEW HOPE
Warner • Johnson • Snyder • Rio • Nelson
ISBN: 1-56971-648-X $12.95
BATTLE OF THE BOUNTY HUNTERS
POP-UP COMIC BOOK
Windham • Moeller
ISBN: 1-56971-129-1 $17.95
DARK FORCES
Prose novellas, heavily illustrated
SOLDIER FOR THE EMPIRE
Dietz • Williams
hardcover edition
ISBN: 1-56971-155-0 $24.95
paperback edition
ISBN: 1-56971-348-0 $14.95
REBEL AGENT
Dietz • Tucker
hardcover edition
ISBN: 1-56971-156-9 $24.95
paperback edition
ISBN: 1-56971-400-2 $14.95
JEDI KNIGHT
Dietz • Dorman
hardcover edition
ISBN: 1-56971-157-7 $24.95
paperback edition
ISBN: 1-56971-433-9 $14.95

SPANS MULTIPLE ERAS

BOUNTY HUNTERS
Truman • Schultz • Stradley • Mangels
ISBN: 1-56971-467-3 $12.95

* New

•*Prices and availability subject to change without notice*

TALES OF THE SITH ERA 25,000-1000
YEARS BEFORE STAR WARS: A NEW HOPE

TALES OF THE JEDI
THE GOLDEN AGE OF THE SITH
Anderson • Carrasco, Jr. • Gossett
ISBN: 1-56971-229-8 $16.95
FALL OF THE SITH EMPIRE
Anderson • Heike • Carrasco, Jr.
ISBN: 1-56971-320-0 $14 .95
KNIGHTS OF THE OLD REPUBLIC
Veitch • Gossett
ISBN: 1-56971-020-1 $14.95
THE FREEDON NADD UPRISING
Veitch • Akins • Rodier
ISBN: 1-56971-307-3 $5.95
DARK LORDS OF THE SITH
Veitch • Anderson • Gossett
ISBN: 1-56971-095-3 $17.95
THE SITH WAR
Anderson • Carrasco, Jr.
ISBN: 1-56971-173-9 $17.95
*REDEMPTION
Anderson • Gossett • Pepoy • McDaniel
ISBN: 1-56971-535-1 $14.95
*JEDI VS. SITH
Macan • Bachs • Fernandez
ISBN: 1-56971-649-8 $15.95

PREQUEL ERA 1000-0 YEARS
BEFORE STAR WARS: A NEW HOPE

*JEDI COUNCIL
ACTS OF WAR
Stradley • Fabbri • Vecchia
ISBN: 1-56971-539-4 $12.95
*DARTH MAUL
Marz • Duursema • Magyar • Struzan
ISBN: 1-56971-542-4 $12.95
PRELUDE TO REBELLION
Strnad • Winn • Jones
ISBN: 1-56971-448-7 $14.95
OUTLANDER
Truman • Leonardi • Rio
ISBN: 1-56971-514-9 $14.95
*JEDI COUNCIL
EMMISSARIES TO MALASTARE
Truman • Duursema • Others
ISBN: 1-56971-545-9 $15.95
STAR WARS: TWILIGHT
Ostrander • Duursema • Magyar
ISBN: 1-56971-558-0 $12.95
EPISODE 1 —
THE PHANTOM MENACE
Gilroy • Damaggio • Williamson
ISBN: 1-56971-359-6 $12.95
EPISODE 1 —
THE PHANTOM MENACE ADVENTURES
ISBN: 1-56971-443-6 $12.95
MANGA EDITIONS
Translated into English
EPISODE 1 — THE PHANTOM MENACE
George Lucas • Kia Asamiya
VOLUME 1
ISBN: 1-56971-483-5 $9.95
VOLUME 2
ISBN: 1-56971-484-3 $9.95
*JANGO FETT
Marz • Fowler
ISBN: 1-56971-623-4 $5.95
*ZAM WESELL
Marz • Naifeh
ISBN: 1-56971-624-2 $5.95
EPISODE 2 —
ATTACK OF THE CLONES
Gilroy • Duursema • Kryssing • McCaig
ISBN: 1-56971-609-8 $17.95
DROIDS
THE KALARBA ADVENTURES
Thorsland • Windham • Gibson
ISBN: 1-56971-064-3 $17.95
REBELLION
Windham • Gibson
ISBN: 1-56971-224-7 $14.95
JABBA THE HUTT
THE ART OF THE DEAL
Woodring • Wetherell • Sheldon
ISBN: 1-56971-310-3 $9.95
*UNDERWORLD
THE YAVIN VASSILIKA
Kennedy • Meglia
ISBN: 1-56971-618-8 $14.95
CLASSIC STAR WARS
HAN SOLO AT STARS' END
Goodwin • Alcala
ISBN: 1-56971-254-0 $6.95
BOBA FETT
ENEMY OF THE EMPIRE
Wagner • Gibson • Nadeau • Ezquerra
ISBN: 1-56971-407-X $12.95

TRILOGY ERA 0-5 YEARS
AFTER STAR WARS: A NEW HOPE

A NEW HOPE SPECIAL EDITION
Jones • Barreto • Williamson
ISBN: 1-56971-213-1 $9.95
MANGA EDITIONS
Translated into English
A NEW HOPE
George Lucas • Hisao Tamaki
VOLUME 1
ISBN: 1-56971-362-6 $9.95
VOLUME 2
ISBN: 1-56971-363-4 $9.95
VOLUME 3
ISBN: 1-56971-364-2 $9.95
VOLUME 4
ISBN: 1-56971-365-0 $9.95
VADER'S QUEST
Macan • Gibbons
ISBN: 1-56971-415-0 $11.95
CLASSIC STAR WARS
THE EARLY ADVENTURES
Manning • Hoberg
ISBN: 1-56971-178-X $19.95
SPLINTER OF THE MIND'S EYE
Austin • Sprouse
ISBN: 1-56971-223-9 $14.95
CLASSIC STAR WARS
IN DEADLY PURSUIT
Goodwin • Williamson
ISBN: 1-56971-109-7 $16.95
THE EMPIRE STRIKES BACK
SPECIAL EDITION
Goodwin • Williamson
ISBN: 1-56971-234-4 $9.95
MANGA EDITIONS
Translated into English
THE EMPIRE STRIKES BACK
George Lucas • Toshiki Kudo
VOLUME 1
ISBN: 1-56971-390-1 $9.95
VOLUME 2
ISBN: 1-56971-391-X $9.95
VOLUME 3
ISBN: 1-56971-392-8 $9.95
VOLUME 4
ISBN: 1-56971-393-6 $9.95
CLASSIC STAR WARS
THE REBEL STORM
Goodwin • Williamson
ISBN: 1-56971-106-2 $16.95
CLASSIC STAR WARS
ESCAPE TO HOTH
Goodwin • Williamson
ISBN: 1-56971-093-7 $16.95
SHADOWS OF THE EMPIRE
SHADOWS OF THE EMPIRE
Wagner • Plunkett • Russell
ISBN: 1-56971-183-6 $17.95
RETURN OF THE JEDI SPECIAL EDITION
Goodwin • Williamson
ISBN: 1-56971-235-2 $9.95
MANGA EDITIONS
Translated into English
RETURN OF THE JEDI
George Lucas • Shin-ichi Hiromoto
VOLUME 1
ISBN: 1-56971-394-4 $9.95
VOLUME 2
ISBN: 1-56971-395-2 $9.95
VOLUME 3
ISBN: 1-56971-396-0 $9.95
VOLUME 4
ISBN: 1-56971-397-9 $9.95

CLASSIC SPIN-OFF ERA 5-25 YEARS
AFTER STAR WARS: A NEW HOPE

MARA JADE
BY THE EMPEROR'S HAND
Zahn • Stackpole • Ezquerra
ISBN: 1-56971-401-0 $15.95
SHADOWS OF THE EMPIRE
EVOLUTION
Perry • Randall • Simmons
ISBN: 1-56971-441-X $14.95
X-WING ROGUE SQUADRON
THE PHANTOM AFFAIR
Stackpole • Macan • Biukovic
ISBN: 1-56971-251-4 $12.95
BATTLEGROUND: TATOOINE
Stackpole • Strnad • Nadeau • Ensign
ISBN: 1-56971-276-X $12.95
THE WARRIOR PRINCESS
Stackpole • Tolson • Nadeau • Ensign
ISBN: 1-56971-330-8 $12.95
REQUIEM FOR A ROGUE
Stackpole • Strnad • Barr • Erskine
ISBN: 1-56971-331-6 $12.95

IN THE EMPIRE'S SERVICE
Stackpole • Nadeau • Ensign
ISBN: 1-56971-383-9 $12.95
BLOOD AND HONOR
Stackpole • Crespo • Hall • Martin
ISBN: 1-56971-387-1 $12.95
MASQUERADE
Stackpole • Johnson • Martin
ISBN: 1-56971-487-8 $12.95
MANDATORY RETIREMENT
Stackpole • Crespo • Nadeau
ISBN: 1-56971-492-4 $12.95
THE THRAWN TRILOGY
HEIR TO THE EMPIRE
Baron • Vatine • Blanchard
ISBN: 1-56971-202-6 $19.95
DARK FORCE RISING
Baron • Dodson • Nowlan
ISBN: 1-56971-269-7 $17.95
THE LAST COMMAND
Baron • Biukovic • Shanower
ISBN: 1-56971-378-2 $17.95
DARK EMPIRE
DARK EMPIRE
Veitch • Kennedy
ISBN: 1-56971-073-2 $17.95
DARK EMPIRE II
Veitch • Kennedy
ISBN: 1-56971-119-4 $17.95
EMPIRE'S END
Veitch • Baikie
ISBN: 1-56971-306-5 $5.95
BOBA FETT
DEATH, LIES, & TREACHERY
Wagner • Kennedy
ISBN: 1-56971-311-1 $12.95
CRIMSON EMPIRE
CRIMSON EMPIRE
Richardson • Stradley • Gulacy • Russell
ISBN: 1-56971-355-3 $17.95
COUNCIL OF BLOOD
Richardson • Stradley • Gulacy • Emberlin
ISBN: 1-56971-410-X $17.95
JEDI ACADEMY
LEVIATHAN
Anderson • Carrasco • Heike
ISBN: 1-56971-456-8 $11.95

THE NEW JEDI ORDER ERA 25+ YEARS
AFTER STAR WARS: A NEW HOPE

UNION
Stackpole • Teranishi • Chuckry
ISBN: 1-56971-464-9 $12.95
CHEWBACCA
Macan • Duursema • Others
ISBN: 1-56971-515-7 $12.95

INFINITIES —
DOES NOT APPLY TO TIMELINE

*TALES VOLUME 1
Marz • Plunkett • Duursema • Others
ISBN: 1-56971-619-6 $19.95
*INFINITIES
A NEW HOPE
Warner • Johnson • Snyder • Rio • Nelson
ISBN: 1-56971-648-X $12.95
BATTLE OF THE BOUNTY HUNTERS
POP-UP COMIC BOOK
Windham • Moeller
ISBN: 1-56971-129-1 $17.95
DARK FORCES
Prose novellas, heavily illustrated
SOLDIER FOR THE EMPIRE
Dietz • Williams
hardcover edition
ISBN: 1-56971-155-0 $24.95
paperback edition
ISBN: 1-56971-348-0 $14.95
REBEL AGENT
Dietz • Tucker
hardcover edition
ISBN: 1-56971-156-9 $24.95
paperback edition
ISBN: 1-56971-400-2 $14.95
JEDI KNIGHT
Dietz • Dorman
hardcover edition
ISBN: 1-56971-157-7 $24.95
paperback edition
ISBN: 1-56971-433-9 $14.95

SPANS MULTIPLE ERAS

BOUNTY HUNTERS
Truman • Schultz • Stradley • Mangels
ISBN: 1-56971-467-3 $12.95

* New
•Prices and availability subject to change without notice

Available from your local comics shop or bookstore!
To find a comics shop in your area, call 1-888-266-4226 • For more information or to order direct: •On the web: www.darkhorse.com • E-mail: mailorder@darkhorse.com
•Phone: 1-800-862-0052 or (503) 652-9701 • Mon.-Sat. 9 A.M. to 5 P.M. Pacific Time   *Prices and availability subject to change without notice